Phonics Reading Program

Clifford's Chick

by Leslie McGuire

Illustrated by Steve Haefele

Based on the books by Norman Bridwell

SCHOLASTIC INC.
New York   Toronto   London   Auckland   Sydney
Mexico City   New Delhi   Hong Kong   Buenos Aires

Clifford wants
some lunch.

He sees an old box.

"I hope there are chips
in here," he says.

He wants chips
to munch.

Clifford checks in the box.

"An egg is in here!" says Clifford.

"Why is an egg in such an old box?"

The egg cracks.

"Oh, no!" says Clifford.

Chirp! Chirp!

A chick pops out
of the egg.

The chick hops
on Clifford's chest.

"Hi, Mom,"
says the chick.

"I am not a mom,"
says Clifford. "I am
a dog."

The chick is very sad.

"Then I do not have a mom," he says.

Clifford says, "I can help you. I will look around for her."

Clifford checks
around the old shed.

He does not see
any moms.

He checks in the back
of an old truck.

He does not see
any moms.

The chick hugs his mom.

The chick is very, very sad.

Just then, there is a big PEEP!

It is the chick's mom!